GW00420431

MY HERO ACADEMIA

Danilo

WWW.DANILO.COM

Published by Danilo Promotions Ltd. Unit 3, The io Centre, Lea Road, Waltham Abbey, EN9 1AS, England.
Enquiries: **info@danilo.com** For all other information: **www.danilo.com**

Printed in China.

PERSONAL INFORMATION

NAME

ADDRESS

MOBILE

EMAIL

IN CASE OF EMERGENCY PLEASE CONTACT

NAME

ADDRESS

MOBILE

DOCTOR

DOCTOR TELEPHONE

KNOWN ALLERGIES

NOTES

JANUARY

WK	M	T	W	T	F	S	S
52							1
1	2	3	4	5	6	7	8
2	9	10	11	12	13	14	15
3	16	17	18	19	20	21	22
4	23	24	25	26	27	28	29
5	30	31					

FEBRUARY

WK	M	T	W	T	F	S	S
5			1	2	3	4	5
6	6	7	8	9	10	11	12
7	13	14	15	16	17	18	19
8	20	21	22	23	24	25	26
9	27	28					

MARCH

WK	M	T	W	T	F	S	S
9			1	2	3	4	5
10	6	7	8	9	10	11	12
11	13	14	15	16	17	18	19
12	20	21	22	23	24	25	26
13	27	28	29	30	31		

APRIL

WK	M	T	W	T	F	S	S
13						1	2
14	3	4	5	6	7	8	9
15	10	11	12	13	14	15	16
16	17	18	19	20	21	22	23
17	24	25	26	27	28	29	30

MAY

WK	M	T	W	T	F	S	S
18	1	2	3	4	5	6	7
19	8	9	10	11	12	13	14
20	15	16	17	18	19	20	21
21	22	23	24	25	26	27	28
22	29	30	31				

JUNE

WK	M	T	W	T	F	S	S
22				1	2	3	4
23	5	6	7	8	9	10	11
24	12	13	14	15	16	17	18
25	19	20	21	22	23	24	25
26	26	27	28	29	30		

JULY

WK	M	T	W	T	F	S	S
26						1	2
27	3	4	5	6	7	8	9
28	10	11	12	13	14	15	16
29	17	18	19	20	21	22	23
30	24	25	26	27	28	29	30
31	31						

AUGUST

WK	M	T	W	T	F	S	S
31		1	2	3	4	5	6
32	7	8	9	10	11	12	13
33	14	15	16	17	18	19	20
34	21	22	23	24	25	26	27
35	28	29	30	31			

SEPTEMBER

WK	M	T	W	T	F	S	S
35					1	2	3
36	4	5	6	7	8	9	10
37	11	12	13	14	15	16	17
38	18	19	20	21	22	23	24
39	25	26	27	28	29	30	

OCTOBER

WK	M	T	W	T	F	S	S
39							1
40	2	3	4	5	6	7	8
41	9	10	11	12	13	14	15
42	16	17	18	19	20	21	22
43	23	24	25	26	27	28	29
44	30	31					

NOVEMBER

WK	M	T	W	T	F	S	S
44			1	2	3	4	5
45	6	7	8	9	10	11	12
46	13	14	15	16	17	18	19
47	20	21	22	23	24	25	26
48	27	28	29	30			

DECEMBER

WK	M	T	W	T	F	S	S
48					1	2	3
49	4	5	6	7	8	9	10
50	11	12	13	14	15	16	17
51	18	19	20	21	22	23	24
52	25	26	27	28	29	30	31

2024 YEAR TO VIEW

JANUARY

WK	M	T	W	T	F	S	S
1	1	2	3	4	5	6	7
2	8	9	10	11	12	13	14
3	15	16	17	18	19	20	21
4	22	23	24	25	26	27	28
5	29	30	31				

FEBRUARY

WK	M	T	W	T	F	S	S
5				1	2	3	4
6	5	6	7	8	9	10	11
7	12	13	14	15	16	17	18
8	19	20	21	22	23	24	25
9	26	27	28	29			

MARCH

WK	M	T	W	T	F	S	S
9					1	2	3
10	4	5	6	7	8	9	10
11	11	12	13	14	15	16	17
12	18	19	20	21	22	23	24
13	25	26	27	28	29	30	31

APRIL

WK	M	T	W	T	F	S	S
14	1	2	3	4	5	6	7
15	8	9	10	11	12	13	14
16	15	16	17	18	19	20	21
17	22	23	24	25	26	27	28
18	29	30					

MAY

WK	M	T	W	T	F	S	S
18			1	2	3	4	5
19	6	7	8	9	10	11	12
20	13	14	15	16	17	18	19
21	20	21	22	23	24	25	26
22	27	28	29	30	31		

JUNE

WK	M	T	W	T	F	S	S
22						1	2
23	3	4	5	6	7	8	9
24	10	11	12	13	14	15	16
25	17	18	19	20	21	22	23
26	24	25	26	27	28	29	30

JULY

WK	M	T	W	T	F	S	S
27	1	2	3	4	5	6	7
28	8	9	10	11	12	13	14
29	15	16	17	18	19	20	21
30	22	23	24	25	26	27	28
31	29	30	31				

AUGUST

WK	M	T	W	T	F	S	S
31				1	2	3	4
32	5	6	7	8	9	10	11
33	12	13	14	15	16	17	18
34	19	20	21	22	23	24	25
35	26	27	28	29	30	31	

SEPTEMBER

WK	M	T	W	T	F	S	S
35							1
36	2	3	4	5	6	7	8
37	9	10	11	12	13	14	15
38	16	17	18	19	20	21	22
39	23	24	25	26	27	28	29
40	30						

OCTOBER

WK	M	T	W	T	F	S	S
40		1	2	3	4	5	6
41	7	8	9	10	11	12	13
42	14	15	16	17	18	19	20
43	21	22	23	24	25	26	27
44	28	29	30	31			

NOVEMBER

WK	M	T	W	T	F	S	S
44					1	2	3
45	4	5	6	7	8	9	10
46	11	12	13	14	15	16	17
47	18	19	20	21	22	23	24
48	25	26	27	28	29	30	

DECEMBER

WK	M	T	W	T	F	S	S
48							1
49	2	3	4	5	6	7	8
50	9	10	11	12	13	14	15
51	16	17	18	19	20	21	22
52	23	24	25	26	27	28	29
1	30	31					

	2023
NEW YEAR'S DAY	JAN 1
NEW YEAR HOLIDAY	JAN 2
BANK HOLIDAY (SCOTLAND)	JAN 3
CHINESE NEW YEAR (RABBIT)	JAN 22
VALENTINE'S DAY	FEB 14
SHROVE TUESDAY	FEB 21
ST. DAVID'S DAY	MAR 1
ST. PATRICK'S DAY	MAR 17
MOTHERING SUNDAY (UK)	MAR 19
RAMADAN BEGINS	MAR 22
DAYLIGHT SAVING TIME STARTS	MAR 26
PASSOVER BEGINS	APR 5
GOOD FRIDAY	APR 7
EASTER SUNDAY	APR 9
EASTER MONDAY	APR 10
EARTH DAY	APR 22
ST. GEORGE'S DAY	APR 23
EARLY MAY BANK HOLIDAY	MAY 1
SPRING BANK HOLIDAY	MAY 29
FATHER'S DAY (UK)	JUN 18
PUBLIC HOLIDAY (NORTHERN IRELAND)	JUL 12
ISLAMIC NEW YEAR BEGINS	JUL 18
SUMMER BANK HOLIDAY (SCOTLAND)	AUG 7
SUMMER BANK HOLIDAY (ENG, NIR, WAL)	AUG 28
ROSH HASHANAH (JEWISH NEW YEAR) BEGINS	SEP 15
INTERNATIONAL DAY OF PEACE (UNITED NATIONS)	SEP 21
YOM KIPPUR BEGINS	SEP 24
WORLD MENTAL HEALTH DAY	OCT 10
DAYLIGHT SAVING TIME ENDS	OCT 29
HALLOWEEN	OCT 31
GUY FAWKES NIGHT	NOV 5
DIWALI / REMEMBRANCE SUNDAY	NOV 12
ST. ANDREW'S DAY	NOV 30
CHRISTMAS DAY	DEC 25
BOXING DAY	DEC 26
NEW YEAR'S EVE	DEC 31

PLANNER 2023

JANUARY	FEBRUARY	MARCH
1 S	1 W	1 W
2 M	2 T	2 T
3 T	3 F	3 F
4 W	4 S	4 S
5 T	5 S	5 S
6 F	6 M	6 M
7 S	7 T	7 T
8 S	8 W	8 W
9 M	9 T	9 T
10 T	10 F	10 F
11 W	11 S	11 S
12 T	12 S	12 S
13 F	13 M	13 M
14 S	14 T	14 T
15 S	15 W	15 W
16 M	16 T	16 T
17 T	17 F	17 F
18 W	18 S	18 S
19 T	19 S	19 S
20 F	20 M	20 M
21 S	21 T	21 T
22 S	22 W	22 W
23 M	23 T	23 T
24 T	24 F	24 F
25 W	25 S	25 S
26 T	26 S	26 S
27 F	27 M	27 M
28 S	28 T	28 T
29 S		29 W
30 M		30 T
31 T		31 F

APRIL	MAY	JUNE
1 S	1 M	1 T
2 S	2 T	2 F
3 M	3 W	3 S
4 T	4 T	4 S
5 W	5 F	5 M
6 T	6 S	6 T
7 F	7 S	7 W
8 S	8 M	8 T
9 S	9 T	9 F
10 M	10 W	10 S
11 T	11 T	11 S
12 W	12 F	12 M
13 T	13 S	13 T
14 F	14 S	14 W
15 S	15 M	15 T
16 S	16 T	16 F
17 M	17 W	17 S
18 T	18 T	18 S
19 W	19 F	19 M
20 T	20 S	20 T
21 F	21 S	21 W
22 S	22 M	22 T
23 S	23 T	23 F
24 M	24 W	24 S
25 T	25 T	25 S
26 W	26 F	26 M
27 T	27 S	27 T
28 F	28 S	28 W
29 S	29 M	29 T
30 S	30 T	30 F
	31 W	

PLANNER 2023

JULY	AUGUST	SEPTEMBER
1 S	1 T	1 F
2 S	2 W	2 S
3 M	3 T	3 S
4 T	4 F	4 M
5 W	5 S	5 T
6 T	6 S	6 W
7 F	7 M	7 T
8 S	8 T	8 F
9 S	9 W	9 S
10 M	10 T	10 S
11 T	11 F	11 M
12 W	12 S	12 T
13 T	13 S	13 W
14 F	14 M	14 T
15 S	15 T	15 F
16 S	16 W	16 S
17 M	17 T	17 S
18 T	18 F	18 M
19 W	19 S	19 T
20 T	20 S	20 W
21 F	21 M	21 T
22 S	22 T	22 F
23 S	23 W	23 S
24 M	24 T	24 S
25 T	25 F	25 M
26 W	26 S	26 T
27 T	27 S	27 W
28 F	28 M	28 T
29 S	29 T	29 F
30 S	30 W	30 S
31 M	31 T	

OCTOBER	NOVEMBER	DECEMBER
1 S	1 W	1 F
2 M	2 T	2 S
3 T	3 F	3 S
4 W	4 S	4 M
5 T	5 S	5 T
6 F	6 M	6 W
7 S	7 T	7 T
8 S	8 W	8 F
9 M	9 T	9 S
10 T	10 F	10 S
11 W	11 S	11 M
12 T	12 S	12 T
13 F	13 M	13 W
14 S	14 T	14 T
15 S	15 W	15 F
16 M	16 T	16 S
17 T	17 F	17 S
18 W	18 S	18 M
19 T	19 S	19 T
20 F	20 M	20 W
21 S	21 T	21 T
22 S	22 W	22 F
23 M	23 T	23 S
24 T	24 F	24 S
25 W	25 S	25 M
26 T	26 S	26 T
27 F	27 M	27 W
28 S	28 T	28 T
29 S	29 W	29 F
30 M	30 T	30 S
31 T		31 S

JANUARY 2023

TO DO

MY HERO ACADEMIA

MY HERO ACADEMIA

僕のヒーローアカデミア

26 MONDAY

27 TUESDAY

28 WEDNESDAY

29 THURSDAY

FRIDAY 30

NEW YEAR'S EVE

SATURDAY 31

NEW YEAR'S DAY

SUNDAY 1

NOTES

T	F	S	S	M	T	W	T	F	S	S	M	T	W	T	F	S	S	M	T	W	T	F	S	S	M	T	W	T	F	S
15	16	17	18	19	20	21	22	23	24	25	26	27	28	29	30	31	1	2	3	4	5	6	7	8	9	10	11	12	13	14

2 MONDAY
NEW YEAR HOLIDAY

3 TUESDAY
BANK HOLIDAY (SCOTLAND)

4 WEDNESDAY

5 THURSDAY

FRIDAY 6

SATURDAY 7

SUNDAY 8

NOTES

S	M	T	W	T	F	S	S	M	T	W	T	F	S	S	M	T	W	T	F	S	S	M	T	W	T	F	S	S	M	T
1	2	3	4	5	6	7	8	9	10	11	12	13	14	15	16	17	18	19	20	21	22	23	24	25	26	27	28	29	30	31

9 MONDAY

10 TUESDAY

11 WEDNESDAY

12 THURSDAY

J

FRIDAY 13

SATURDAY 14

SUNDAY 15

NOTES

S	M	T	W	T	F	S	S	M	T	W	T	F	S	S	M	T	W	T	F	S	S	M	T	W	T	F	S	S	M	T
1	2	3	4	5	6	7	8	9	10	11	12	13	14	15	16	17	18	19	20	21	22	23	24	25	26	27	28	29	30	31

16 MONDAY

17 TUESDAY

18 WEDNESDAY

19 THURSDAY

FRIDAY 20

SATURDAY 21

CHINESE NEW YEAR (RABBIT)

SUNDAY 22

NOTES

MY HERO ACADEMIA

S	M	T	W	T	F	S	S	M	T	W	T	F	S	S	M	T	W	T	F	S	S	M	T	W	T	F	S	S	M	T
1	2	3	4	5	6	7	8	9	10	11	12	13	14	15	16	17	18	19	20	21	22	23	24	25	26	27	28	29	30	31

23 MONDAY

24 TUESDAY

25 WEDNESDAY

26 THURSDAY

J

FRIDAY 27

SATURDAY 28

SUNDAY 29

NOTES

S	M	T	W	T	F	S	S	M	T	W	T	F	S	S	M	T	W	T	F	S	S	M	T	W	T	F	S	S	M	T
1	2	3	4	5	6	7	8	9	10	11	12	13	14	15	16	17	18	19	20	21	22	23	24	25	26	27	28	29	30	31

FEBRUARY 2023

TO DO

MY HERO ACADEMIA

MY HERO ACADEMIA

僕のヒーローアカデミア

30 MONDAY

31 TUESDAY

1 WEDNESDAY

2 THURSDAY

FRIDAY 3

SATURDAY 4

SUNDAY 5

NOTES

M	T	W	T	F	S	S	M	T	W	T	F	S	S	M	T	W	T	F	S	S	M	T	W	T	F	S	S	M	T	W
16	17	18	19	20	21	22	23	24	25	26	27	28	29	30	31	1	2	3	4	5	6	7	8	9	10	11	12	13	14	15

6 MONDAY

7 TUESDAY

8 WEDNESDAY

9 THURSDAY

FRIDAY 10

SATURDAY 11

SUNDAY 12

NOTES

W	T	F	S	S	M	T	W	T	F	S	S	M	T	W	T	F	S	S	M	T	W	T	F	S	S	M	T
1	2	3	4	5	6	7	8	9	10	11	12	13	14	15	16	17	18	19	20	21	22	23	24	25	26	27	28

13 MONDAY

14 TUESDAY

VALENTINE'S DAY

15 WEDNESDAY

16 THURSDAY

FRIDAY 17

SATURDAY 18

SUNDAY 19

NOTES

W	T	F	S	S	M	T	W	T	F	S	S	M	T	W	T	F	S	S	M	T	W	T	F	S	S	M	T
1	2	3	4	5	6	7	8	9	10	11	12	13	14	15	16	17	18	19	20	21	22	23	24	25	26	27	28

20 MONDAY

21 TUESDAY

SHROVE TUESDAY

22 WEDNESDAY

23 THURSDAY

F

FRIDAY 24

SATURDAY 25

SUNDAY 26

NOTES

W	T	F	S	S	M	T	W	T	F	S	S	M	T	W	T	F	S	S	M	T	W	T	F	S	S	M	T
1	2	3	4	5	6	7	8	9	10	11	12	13	14	15	16	17	18	19	20	21	22	23	24	25	26	27	28

TO DO

MY HERO ACADEMIA

27 MONDAY

28 TUESDAY

1 WEDNESDAY

ST. DAVID'S DAY

2 THURSDAY

FRIDAY 3

SATURDAY 4

SUNDAY 5

NOTES

W	T	F	S	S	M	T	W	T	F	S	S	M	T	W	T	F	S	S	M	T	W	T	F	S	S	M	T
5	16	17	18	19	20	21	22	23	24	25	26	27	28	1	2	3	4	5	6	7	8	9	10	11	12	13	14

6 MONDAY

7 TUESDAY

8 WEDNESDAY

9 THURSDAY

FRIDAY 10

SATURDAY 11

SUNDAY 12

NOTES

W	T	F	S	S	M	T	W	T	F	S	S	M	T	W	T	F	S	S	M	T	W	T	F	S	S	M	T	W	T	F
1	2	3	4	5	6	7	8	9	10	11	12	13	14	15	16	17	18	19	20	21	22	23	24	25	26	27	28	29	30	31

13 MONDAY

14 TUESDAY

15 WEDNESDAY

16 THURSDAY

ST. PATRICK'S DAY

FRIDAY 17

SATURDAY 18

MOTHERING SUNDAY (UK)

SUNDAY 19

NOTES

MY HERO ACADEMIA

W	T	F	S	S	M	T	W	T	F	S	S	M	T	W	T	F	S	S	M	T	W	T	F	S	S	M	T	W	T	F
1	2	3	4	5	6	7	8	9	10	11	12	13	14	15	16	17	18	19	20	21	22	23	24	25	26	27	28	29	30	31

20 MONDAY

21 TUESDAY

22 WEDNESDAY

RAMADAN BEGINS

23 THURSDAY

FRIDAY 24

SATURDAY 25

DAYLIGHT SAVING TIME STARTS

SUNDAY 26

NOTES

W	T	F	S	S	M	T	W	T	F	S	S	M	T	W	T	F	S	S	M	T	W	T	F	S	S	M	T	W	T	F
1	2	3	4	5	6	7	8	9	10	11	12	13	14	15	16	17	18	19	20	21	22	23	24	25	26	27	28	29	30	31

MY HERO ACADEMIA

僕のヒーローアカデミア

APRIL 2023

TO DO

MY HERO ACADEMIA

27 MONDAY

28 TUESDAY

29 WEDNESDAY

30 THURSDAY

FRIDAY 31

SATURDAY 1

SUNDAY 2

NOTES

T	F	S	S	M	T	W	T	F	S	S	M	T	W	T	F	S	S	M	T	W	T	F	S	S	M	T	W	T	F	S
16	17	18	19	20	21	22	23	24	25	26	27	28	29	30	31	1	2	3	4	5	6	7	8	9	10	11	12	13	14	15

3 MONDAY

4 TUESDAY

5 WEDNESDAY

PASSOVER BEGINS

6 THURSDAY

GOOD FRIDAY

FRIDAY 7

SATURDAY 8

EASTER SUNDAY

SUNDAY 9

NOTES

MY HERO ACADEMIA

S	S	M	T	W	T	F	S	S	M	T	W	T	F	S	S	M	T	W	T	F	S	S	M	T	W	T	F	S	S
1	2	3	4	5	6	7	8	9	10	11	12	13	14	15	16	17	18	19	20	21	22	23	24	25	26	27	28	29	30

10 MONDAY

EASTER MONDAY

11 TUESDAY

12 WEDNESDAY

13 THURSDAY

FRIDAY 14

SATURDAY 15

SUNDAY 16

NOTES

S	S	M	T	W	T	F	S	S	M	T	W	T	F	S	S	M	T	W	T	F	S	S	M	T	W	T	F	S	S
1	2	3	4	5	6	7	8	9	10	11	12	13	14	15	16	17	18	19	20	21	22	23	24	25	26	27	28	29	30

17 MONDAY

18 TUESDAY

19 WEDNESDAY

20 THURSDAY

FRIDAY 21

EARTH DAY

SATURDAY 22

ST. GEORGE'S DAY

SUNDAY 23

NOTES

S	S	M	T	W	T	F	S	S	M	T	W	T	F	S	S	M	T	W	T	F	S	S	M	T	W	T	F	S	S
1	2	3	4	5	6	7	8	9	10	11	12	13	14	15	16	17	18	19	20	21	22	23	24	25	26	27	28	29	30

A

24 MONDAY

25 TUESDAY

26 WEDNESDAY

27 THURSDAY

FRIDAY 28

SATURDAY 29

SUNDAY 30

NOTES

S	S	M	T	W	T	F	S	S	M	T	W	T	F	S	S	M	T	W	T	F	S	S	M	T	W	T	F	S	S
1	2	3	4	5	6	7	8	9	10	11	12	13	14	15	16	17	18	19	20	21	22	23	24	25	26	27	28	29	30

MAY 2023
TO DO
MY HERO
ACADEMIA

MY HERO
ACADEMIA
僕のヒーローアカデミア

1 MONDAY

EARLY MAY BANK HOLIDAY

2 TUESDAY

3 WEDNESDAY

4 THURSDAY

FRIDAY 5

SATURDAY 6

SUNDAY 7

NOTES

M	T	W	T	F	S	S	M	T	W	T	F	S	S	M	T	W	T	F	S	S	M	T	W	T	F	S	S	M	T	W
1	2	3	4	5	6	7	8	9	10	11	12	13	14	15	16	17	18	19	20	21	22	23	24	25	26	27	28	29	30	31

8 MONDAY

9 TUESDAY

10 WEDNESDAY

11 THURSDAY

FRIDAY 12

SATURDAY 13

SUNDAY 14

NOTES

M	T	W	T	F	S	S	M	T	W	T	F	S	S	M	T	W	T	F	S	S	M	T	W	T	F	S	S	M	T	W
1	2	3	4	5	6	7	8	9	10	11	12	13	14	15	16	17	18	19	20	21	22	23	24	25	26	27	28	29	30	31

15 MONDAY

16 TUESDAY

17 WEDNESDAY

18 THURSDAY

FRIDAY 19

SATURDAY 20

SUNDAY 21

NOTES

M	T	W	T	F	S	S	M	T	W	T	F	S	S	M	T	W	T	F	S	S	M	T	W	T	F	S	S	M	T	W
1	2	3	4	5	6	7	8	9	10	11	12	13	14	15	16	17	18	19	20	21	22	23	24	25	26	27	28	29	30	31

M

22 MONDAY

23 TUESDAY

24 WEDNESDAY

25 THURSDAY

FRIDAY 26

SATURDAY 27

SUNDAY 28

NOTES

M	T	W	T	F	S	S	M	T	W	T	F	S	S	M	T	W	T	F	S	S	M	T	W	T	F	S	S	M	T	W
1	2	3	4	5	6	7	8	9	10	11	12	13	14	15	16	17	18	19	20	21	22	23	24	25	26	27	28	29	30	31

JUNE 2023

TO DO

MY HERO ACADEMIA

MY HERO ACADEMIA

僕のヒーローアカデミア

29 MONDAY

SPRING BANK HOLIDAY

30 TUESDAY

31 WEDNESDAY

1 THURSDAY

FRIDAY 2

SATURDAY 3

SUNDAY 4

NOTES

T	W	T	F	S	S	M	T	W	T	F	S	S	M	T	W	T	F	S	S	M	T	W	T	F	S	S	M	T	W	T
16	17	18	19	20	21	22	23	24	25	26	27	28	29	30	31	1	2	3	4	5	6	7	8	9	10	11	12	13	14	15

5 MONDAY

6 TUESDAY

7 WEDNESDAY

8 THURSDAY

FRIDAY 9

SATURDAY 10

SUNDAY 11

NOTES

T	F	S	S	M	T	W	T	F	S	S	M	T	W	T	F	S	S	M	T	W	T	F	S	S	M	T	W	T	F
1	2	3	4	5	6	7	8	9	10	11	12	13	14	15	16	17	18	19	20	21	22	23	24	25	26	27	28	29	30

12 MONDAY

13 TUESDAY

14 WEDNESDAY

15 THURSDAY

FRIDAY **16**

SATURDAY **17**

SUNDAY **18**

FATHER'S DAY (UK)

NOTES

T	F	S	S	M	T	W	T	F	S	S	M	T	W	T	F	S	S	M	T	W	T	F	S	S	M	T	W	T	F
1	2	3	4	5	6	7	8	9	10	11	12	13	14	15	16	17	18	19	20	21	22	23	24	25	26	27	28	29	30

19 MONDAY

20 TUESDAY

21 WEDNESDAY

22 THURSDAY

FRIDAY 23

SATURDAY 24

SUNDAY 25

NOTES

T	F	S	S	M	T	W	T	F	S	S	M	T	W	T	F	S	S	M	T	W	T	F	S	S	M	T	W	T	F
1	2	3	4	5	6	7	8	9	10	11	12	13	14	15	16	17	18	19	20	21	22	23	24	25	26	27	28	29	30

J

JULY 2023

TO DO

MY HERO ACADEMIA

26 MONDAY

27 TUESDAY

28 WEDNESDAY

29 THURSDAY

FRIDAY 30

SATURDAY 1

SUNDAY 2

NOTES

F	S	S	M	T	W	T	F	S	S	M	T	W	T	F	S	S	M	T	W	T	F	S	S	M	T	W	T	F	S
16	17	18	19	20	21	22	23	24	25	26	27	28	29	30	1	2	3	4	5	6	7	8	9	10	11	12	13	14	15

J

3 MONDAY

4 TUESDAY

5 WEDNESDAY

6 THURSDAY

FRIDAY 7

SATURDAY 8

SUNDAY 9

NOTES

S	S	M	T	W	T	F	S	S	M	T	W	T	F	S	S	M	T	W	T	F	S	S	M	T	W	T	F	S	S	M
1	2	3	4	5	6	7	8	9	10	11	12	13	14	15	16	17	18	19	20	21	22	23	24	25	26	27	28	29	30	31

10 MONDAY

11 TUESDAY

12 WEDNESDAY

PUBLIC HOLIDAY (NORTHERN IRELAND)

13 THURSDAY

FRIDAY 14

SATURDAY 15

SUNDAY 16

NOTES

S	S	M	T	W	T	F	S	S	M	T	W	T	F	S	S	M	T	W	T	F	S	S	M	T	W	T	F	S	S	M
1	2	3	4	5	6	7	8	9	10	11	12	13	14	15	16	17	18	19	20	21	22	23	24	25	26	27	28	29	30	31

J

17 MONDAY

18 TUESDAY

ISLAMIC NEW YEAR BEGINS

19 WEDNESDAY

20 THURSDAY

FRIDAY **21**

SATURDAY **22**

SUNDAY **23**

NOTES

S	S	M	T	W	T	F	S	S	M	T	W	T	F	S	S	M	T	W	T	F	S	S	M	T	W	T	F	S	S	M
1	2	3	4	5	6	7	8	9	10	11	12	13	14	15	16	17	18	19	20	21	22	23	24	25	26	27	28	29	30	31

24 MONDAY

25 TUESDAY

26 WEDNESDAY

27 THURSDAY

FRIDAY 28

SATURDAY 29

SUNDAY 30

NOTES

S	S	M	T	W	T	F	S	S	M	T	W	T	F	S	S	M	T	W	T	F	S	S	M	T	W	T	F	S	S	M
1	2	3	4	5	6	7	8	9	10	11	12	13	14	15	16	17	18	19	20	21	22	23	24	25	26	27	28	29	30	31

AUGUST 2023

TO DO

MY HERO ACADEMIA

MY HERO ACADEMIA

僕のヒーローアカデミア

31 MONDAY

1 TUESDAY

2 WEDNESDAY

3 THURSDAY

FRIDAY 4

SATURDAY 5

SUNDAY 6

A

NOTES

S	M	T	W	T	F	S	S	M	T	W	T	F	S	S	M	T	W	T	F	S	S	M	T	W	T	F	S	S	M	T
16	17	18	19	20	21	22	23	24	25	26	27	28	29	30	31	1	2	3	4	5	6	7	8	9	10	11	12	13	14	15

7 MONDAY

SUMMER BANK HOLIDAY (SCOTLAND)

8 TUESDAY

9 WEDNESDAY

10 THURSDAY

FRIDAY 11

SATURDAY 12

SUNDAY 13

NOTES

T	W	T	F	S	S	M	T	W	T	F	S	S	M	T	W	T	F	S	S	M	T	W	T	F	S	S	M	T	W	T
1	2	3	4	5	6	7	8	9	10	11	12	13	14	15	16	17	18	19	20	21	22	23	24	25	26	27	28	29	30	31

14 MONDAY

15 TUESDAY

16 WEDNESDAY

17 THURSDAY

FRIDAY 18

SATURDAY 19

SUNDAY 20

A

NOTES

T	W	T	F	S	S	M	T	W	T	F	S	S	M	T	W	T	F	S	S	M	T	W	T	F	S	S	M	T	W	T
1	2	3	4	5	6	7	8	9	10	11	12	13	14	15	16	17	18	19	20	21	22	23	24	25	26	27	28	29	30	31

21 MONDAY

22 TUESDAY

23 WEDNESDAY

24 THURSDAY

FRIDAY 25

SATURDAY 26

SUNDAY 27

A

NOTES

T	W	T	F	S	S	M	T	W	T	F	S	S	M	T	W	T	F	S	S	M	T	W	T	F	S	S	M	T	W	T
1	2	3	4	5	6	7	8	9	10	11	12	13	14	15	16	17	18	19	20	21	22	23	24	25	26	27	28	29	30	31

SEPTEMBER 2023

TO DO

MY HERO ACADEMIA

MY HERO ACADEMIA

僕のヒーローアカデミア

28 MONDAY

SUMMER BANK HOLIDAY (ENG, NIR, WAL)

29 TUESDAY

30 WEDNESDAY

31 THURSDAY

FRIDAY 1

SATURDAY 2

SUNDAY 3

S

NOTES

W	T	F	S	S	M	T	W	T	F	S	S	M	T	W	T	F	S	S	M	T	W	T	F	S	S	M	T	W	T	F
16	17	18	19	20	21	22	23	24	25	26	27	28	29	30	31	1	2	3	4	5	6	7	8	9	10	11	12	13	14	15

4 MONDAY

5 TUESDAY

6 WEDNESDAY

7 THURSDAY

FRIDAY 8

SATURDAY 9

SUNDAY 10

NOTES

F	S	S	M	T	W	T	F	S	S	M	T	W	T	F	S	S	M	T	W	T	F	S	S	M	T	W	T	F	S
1	2	3	4	5	6	7	8	9	10	11	12	13	14	15	16	17	18	19	20	21	22	23	24	25	26	27	28	29	30

11 MONDAY

12 TUESDAY

13 WEDNESDAY

14 THURSDAY

FRIDAY 15

ROSH HASHANAH (JEWISH NEW YEAR) BEGINS

SATURDAY 16

SUNDAY 17

NOTES

MY HERO ACADEMIA

F	S	S	M	T	W	T	F	S	S	M	T	W	T	F	S	S	M	T	W	T	F	S	S	M	T	W	T	F	S
1	2	3	4	5	6	7	8	9	10	11	12	13	14	15	16	17	18	19	20	21	22	23	24	25	26	27	28	29	30

S

18 MONDAY

19 TUESDAY

20 WEDNESDAY

21 THURSDAY

INTERNATIONAL DAY OF PEACE (UNITED NATIONS)

FRIDAY 22

SATURDAY 23

SUNDAY 24

YOM KIPPUR BEGINS

NOTES

F	S	S	M	T	W	T	F	S	S	M	T	W	T	F	S	S	M	T	W	T	F	S	S	M	T	W	T	F	S
1	2	3	4	5	6	7	8	9	10	11	12	13	14	15	16	17	18	19	20	21	22	23	24	25	26	27	28	29	30

OCTOBER 2023

TO DO

MY HERO ACADEMIA

MY HERO ACADEMIA

僕のヒーローアカデミア

25 MONDAY

26 TUESDAY

27 WEDNESDAY

28 THURSDAY

FRIDAY 29

SATURDAY 30

SUNDAY 1

NOTES

S	S	M	T	W	T	F	S	S	M	T	W	T	F	S	S	M	T	W	T	F	S	S	M	T	W	T	F	S	S
16	17	18	19	20	21	22	23	24	25	26	27	28	29	30	1	2	3	4	5	6	7	8	9	10	11	12	13	14	15

2 MONDAY

3 TUESDAY

4 WEDNESDAY

5 THURSDAY

FRIDAY 6

SATURDAY 7

SUNDAY 8

NOTES

S	M	T	W	T	F	S	S	M	T	W	T	F	S	S	M	T	W	T	F	S	S	M	T	W	T	F	S	S	M	T
1	2	3	4	5	6	7	8	9	10	11	12	13	14	15	16	17	18	19	20	21	22	23	24	25	26	27	28	29	30	31

9 MONDAY

10 TUESDAY

WORLD MENTAL HEALTH DAY

11 WEDNESDAY

12 THURSDAY

FRIDAY 13

SATURDAY 14

SUNDAY 15

NOTES

S	M	T	W	T	F	S	S	M	T	W	T	F	S	S	M	T	W	T	F	S	S	M	T	W	T	F	S	S	M	T
1	2	3	4	5	6	7	8	9	10	11	12	13	14	15	16	17	18	19	20	21	22	23	24	25	26	27	28	29	30	31

16 MONDAY

17 TUESDAY

18 WEDNESDAY

19 THURSDAY

FRIDAY 20

SATURDAY 21

SUNDAY 22

NOTES

S	M	T	W	T	F	S	S	M	T	W	T	F	S	S	M	T	W	T	F	S	S	M	T	W	T	F	S	S	M	T
1	2	3	4	5	6	7	8	9	10	11	12	13	14	15	16	17	18	19	20	21	22	23	24	25	26	27	28	29	30	31

23 MONDAY

24 TUESDAY

25 WEDNESDAY

26 THURSDAY

FRIDAY 27

SATURDAY 28

DAYLIGHT SAVING TIME ENDS

SUNDAY 29

NOTES

S	M	T	W	T	F	S	S	M	T	W	T	F	S	S	M	T	W	T	F	S	S	M	T	W	T	F	S	S	M	T
1	2	3	4	5	6	7	8	9	10	11	12	13	14	15	16	17	18	19	20	21	22	23	24	25	26	27	28	29	30	31

NOVEMBER 2023

TO DO

MY HERO ACADEMIA

30 MONDAY

31 TUESDAY

HALLOWEEN

1 WEDNESDAY

2 THURSDAY

FRIDAY 3

SATURDAY 4

GUY FAWKES NIGHT

SUNDAY 5

NOTES

MY HERO ACADEMIA

M	T	W	T	F	S	S	M	T	W	T	F	S	S	M	T	W	T	F	S	S	M	T	W	T	F	S	S	M	T	W
16	17	18	19	20	21	22	23	24	25	26	27	28	29	30	31	1	2	3	4	5	6	7	8	9	10	11	12	13	14	15

6 MONDAY

7 TUESDAY

8 WEDNESDAY

9 THURSDAY

FRIDAY **10**

SATURDAY **11**

DIWALI & REMEMBRANCE SUNDAY

SUNDAY **12**

NOTES

W	T	F	S	S	M	T	W	T	F	S	S	M	T	W	T	F	S	S	M	T	W	T	F	S	S	M	T	W	T
1	2	3	4	5	6	7	8	9	10	11	12	13	14	15	16	17	18	19	20	21	22	23	24	25	26	27	28	29	30

13 MONDAY

14 TUESDAY

15 WEDNESDAY

16 THURSDAY

FRIDAY 17

SATURDAY 18

SUNDAY 19

NOTES

W	T	F	S	S	M	T	W	T	F	S	S	M	T	W	T	F	S	S	M	T	W	T	F	S	S	M	T	W	T
1	2	3	4	5	6	7	8	9	10	11	12	13	14	15	16	17	18	19	20	21	22	23	24	25	26	27	28	29	30

20 MONDAY

21 TUESDAY

22 WEDNESDAY

23 THURSDAY

FRIDAY 24

SATURDAY 25

SUNDAY 26

NOTES

W	T	F	S	S	M	T	W	T	F	S	S	M	T	W	T	F	S	S	M	T	W	T	F	S	S	M	T	W	T
1	2	3	4	5	6	7	8	9	10	11	12	13	14	15	16	17	18	19	20	21	22	23	24	25	26	27	28	29	30

DECEMBER 2023

TO DO

MY HERO ACADEMIA

27 MONDAY

28 TUESDAY

29 WEDNESDAY

30 THURSDAY

ST. ANDREW'S DAY

FRIDAY 1

SATURDAY 2

SUNDAY 3

NOTES

MY HERO ACADEMIA

T	F	S	S	M	T	W	T	F	S	S	M	T	W	T	F	S	S	M	T	W	T	F	S	S	M	T	W	T	F
16	17	18	19	20	21	22	23	24	25	26	27	28	29	30	1	2	3	4	5	6	7	8	9	10	11	12	13	14	15

4 MONDAY

5 TUESDAY

6 WEDNESDAY

7 THURSDAY

FRIDAY 8

SATURDAY 9

SUNDAY 10

NOTES

F	S	S	M	T	W	T	F	S	S	M	T	W	T	F	S	S	M	T	W	T	F	S	S	M	T	W	T	F	S	S
1	2	3	4	5	6	7	8	9	10	11	12	13	14	15	16	17	18	19	20	21	22	23	24	25	26	27	28	29	30	31

11 MONDAY

12 TUESDAY

13 WEDNESDAY

14 THURSDAY

FRIDAY 15

SATURDAY 16

SUNDAY 17

NOTES

F	S	S	M	T	W	T	F	S	S	M	T	W	T	F	S	S	M	T	W	T	F	S	S	M	T	W	T	F	S	S
1	2	3	4	5	6	7	8	9	10	11	12	13	14	15	16	17	18	19	20	21	22	23	24	25	26	27	28	29	30	31

18 MONDAY

19 TUESDAY

20 WEDNESDAY

21 THURSDAY

DECEMBER 2023

FRIDAY 22

SATURDAY 23

SUNDAY 24

NOTES

F	S	S	M	T	W	T	F	S	S	M	T	W	T	F	S	S	M	T	W	T	F	S	S	M	T	W	T	F	S	S
1	2	3	4	5	6	7	8	9	10	11	12	13	14	15	16	17	18	19	20	21	22	23	24	25	26	27	28	29	30	31

D

25 MONDAY
CHRISTMAS DAY

26 TUESDAY
BOXING DAY

27 WEDNESDAY

28 THURSDAY

FRIDAY 29

SATURDAY 30

SUNDAY 31

NEW YEAR'S EVE

NOTES

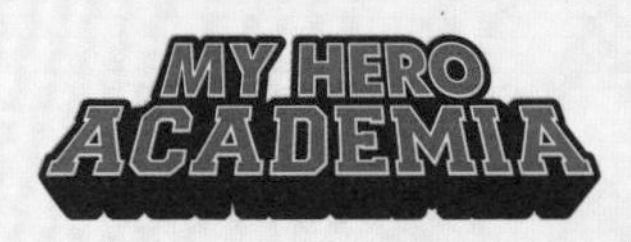

F	S	S	M	T	W	T	F	S	S	M	T	W	T	F	S	S	M	T	W	T	F	S	S	M	T	W	T	F	S	S
1	2	3	4	5	6	7	8	9	10	11	12	13	14	15	16	17	18	19	20	21	22	23	24	25	26	27	28	29	30	31

PLANNER 2024

JANUARY	FEBRUARY	MARCH
1 M	1 T	1 F
2 T	2 F	2 S
3 W	3 S	3 S
4 T	4 S	4 M
5 F	5 M	5 T
6 S	6 T	6 W
7 S	7 W	7 T
8 M	8 T	8 F
9 T	9 F	9 S
10 W	10 S	10 S
11 T	11 S	11 M
12 F	12 M	12 T
13 S	13 T	13 W
14 S	14 W	14 T
15 M	15 T	15 F
16 T	16 F	16 S
17 W	17 S	17 S
18 T	18 S	18 M
19 F	19 M	19 T
20 S	20 T	20 W
21 S	21 W	21 T
22 M	22 T	22 F
23 T	23 F	23 S
24 W	24 S	24 S
25 T	25 S	25 M
26 F	26 M	26 T
27 S	27 T	27 W
28 S	28 W	28 T
29 M	29 T	29 F
30 T		30 S
31 W		31 S

APRIL

1 M
2 T
3 W
4 T
5 F
6 S
7 S
8 M
9 T
10 W
11 T
12 F
13 S
14 S
15 M
16 T
17 W
18 T
19 F
20 S
21 S
22 M
23 T
24 W
25 T
26 F
27 S
28 S
29 M
30 T

MAY

1 W
2 T
3 F
4 S
5 S
6 M
7 T
8 W
9 T
10 F
11 S
12 S
13 M
14 T
15 W
16 T
17 F
18 S
19 S
20 M
21 T
22 W
23 T
24 F
25 S
26 S
27 M
28 T
29 W
30 T
31 F

JUNE

1 S
2 S
3 M
4 T
5 W
6 T
7 F
8 S
9 S
10 M
11 T
12 W
13 T
14 F
15 S
16 S
17 M
18 T
19 W
20 T
21 F
22 S
23 S
24 M
25 T
26 W
27 T
28 F
29 S
30 S

PLANNER 2024

JULY	AUGUST	SEPTEMBER
1 M	1 T	1 S
2 T	2 F	2 M
3 W	3 S	3 T
4 T	4 S	4 W
5 F	5 M	5 T
6 S	6 T	6 F
7 S	7 W	7 S
8 M	8 T	8 S
9 T	9 F	9 M
10 W	10 S	10 T
11 T	11 S	11 W
12 F	12 M	12 T
13 S	13 T	13 F
14 S	14 W	14 S
15 M	15 T	15 S
16 T	16 F	16 M
17 W	17 S	17 T
18 T	18 S	18 W
19 F	19 M	19 T
20 S	20 T	20 F
21 S	21 W	21 S
22 M	22 T	22 S
23 T	23 F	23 M
24 W	24 S	24 T
25 T	25 S	25 W
26 F	26 M	26 T
27 S	27 T	27 F
28 S	28 W	28 S
29 M	29 T	29 S
30 T	30 F	30 M
31 W	31 S	

OCTOBER

1 T
2 W
3 T
4 F
5 S
6 S
7 M
8 T
9 W
10 T
11 F
12 S
13 S
14 M
15 T
16 W
17 T
18 F
19 S
20 S
21 M
22 T
23 W
24 T
25 F
26 S
27 S
28 M
29 T
30 W
31 T

NOVEMBER

1 F
2 S
3 S
4 M
5 T
6 W
7 T
8 F
9 S
10 S
11 M
12 T
13 W
14 T
15 F
16 S
17 S
18 M
19 T
20 W
21 T
22 F
23 S
24 S
25 M
26 T
27 W
28 T
29 F
30 S

DECEMBER

1 S
2 M
3 T
4 W
5 T
6 F
7 S
8 S
9 M
10 T
11 W
12 T
13 F
14 S
15 S
16 M
17 T
18 W
19 T
20 F
21 S
22 S
23 M
24 T
25 W
26 T
27 F
28 S
29 S
30 M
31 T

ADDRESS / PHONE NUMBERS

NAME

ADDRESS

TELEPHONE MOBILE

EMAIL

NAME

ADDRESS

TELEPHONE MOBILE

EMAIL

NAME

ADDRESS

TELEPHONE MOBILE

EMAIL

NAME

ADDRESS

TELEPHONE MOBILE

EMAIL

NAME

ADDRESS

TELEPHONE MOBILE

EMAIL

NAME

ADDRESS

TELEPHONE MOBILE

EMAIL

ADDRESS / PHONE NUMBERS

NAME

ADDRESS

TELEPHONE MOBILE

EMAIL

NAME

ADDRESS

TELEPHONE MOBILE

EMAIL

NAME

ADDRESS

TELEPHONE MOBILE

EMAIL

NAME

ADDRESS

TELEPHONE MOBILE

EMAIL

NAME

ADDRESS

TELEPHONE MOBILE

EMAIL

NAME

ADDRESS

TELEPHONE MOBILE

EMAIL

NOTES

NOTES

NOTES

NOTES

MY HERO
ACADEMIA